C000064210

The Anson

GAS AND OIL ENGINE MUSEUM

(LES CAWLEY'S DREAM)

Campbell Awaiting Restoration

Compiled by Raymond Maddock

© ANSON MUSEUM TRUST LTD 2005

All rights reserved.
Any use of this book in any form needs the permission of both author and publisher
ISBN 1904546 30 7

ANSON MUSEUM TRUST LTD

(Registered charity number 518587.)
Anson Road, Poynton, Cheshire, SK12 1TD.

Patron.
Sir Nicholas Winterton M.P.

Chairman and Curator.
Geoffrey Challinor.

Secretary.
John Davidson.

Treasurer.
John Leigh.

Telephone number 01625 874426

E-Mail Address: Geoff@enginemuseum.org
Website www.enginemuseum.org

ACKNOWLEDGEMENTS.

This book has been compiled as a tribute to the late Les Cawley. Whilst his museum will live on this tribute to my good friend Les is to ensure that he is not forgotten and that his name will go down in history as the founder of a great museum.

Profit from the sales of this book will go toward the running costs of the museum and to support the trust in its work to further honour the work of Les.

I wish to acknowledge the assistance given to me in the production of this book by the following.

Brian Ollier photographic studios for the taking of the photographs and for some of the art work.

My niece Susan who assisted with the typing and proof reading.

Geoffrey Challinor for the loan of photographs and other material from the museum archives.

Eric and Norris whose cartoons are borrowed from their calendars to raise funds for the museum.

To anyone else who has given assistance but whose name has been inadvertently omitted.

Cover: Astle Park Steam Rally 1977 with Les Cawley and Geoff Challinor

CONTENTS

Further Cartoons by Eric and Norris

Stone Table

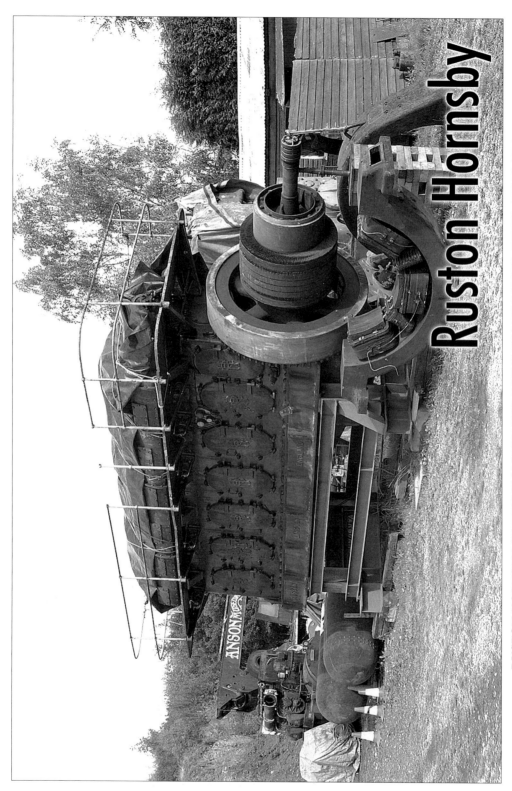

Ruston Hornsby

RUSTON HORNSBY OF LINCOLN TYPE VKR BUILT 1930 TO POWER GENERATING SET FOR EALING STUDIOS. ASSEMBLY WEIGHS 60 TONS.

THE ANSON MUSEUM

The Anson Museum is open to the public at weekends during the summer months and visitors are made most welcome.

The museum is located on the site of the old Anson Colliery at Poynton, near Stockport, Cheshire in the UK. The museum is the home of a unique collection of oil and gas engines which aims to display the development of the internal combustion engine from its earliest beginnings, and also contains a collection of local industrial archaeology.

The museum is the result of founder Les Cawley's years of hard work collecting and restoring engines and his dream of displaying them for a wider audience to see and appreciate. The museum opened to the public in 1990 following sterling efforts by Les and his close friend Geoff Challinor to bring Les's dream to fruition. All the more astounding as it had been done without one penny of public money being spent.

You will see a display of oil and gas engines, mainly from the Manchester area, with some from farther afield.

The museum consists of three public areas; the main building and its annex, the local history building and the outside exhibits. We also have a workshop, internal & external storage areas and our generating house.

We would like you to enjoy your visit. Feel free to wander at will, but take care in the outside exhibit area as there are some uneven surfaces. Please do not hesitate to ask any of the volunteers for information or assistance.

The museum site prior to the start of building showing the slag heap.

PHOTOGRAPH TAKEN OF LES AT THE TURN OF THE CENTURY AND USED ON THE
COVER OF A LEAFLET ADVERTISING THE MUSEUM.

LESLIE (LES) CAWLEY

Les was born in 1919 at 215 Stockport Road, Ardwick, Manchester. His father, Edwin Craven Cawley, had apparently been a seaman and also a grocer, but at the time of Les's birth he was an iron driller at Gorton Tank. His grandfather was William Cawley, of Stapeley Hall, Nantwich, and the family claims descent from Will Cawley, one of the jurymen who signed the death warrant at the trial of King Charles 1st.

His mother was Gertrude Flook before marriage. She died when Les was only 4 years old, his father remarried and, together with brothers, the family moved to Poynton in 1924.

Les did the usual lads' pursuits - making 'rickers'; climbing trees and throwing snowballs at the Co-op clock, which was attached to the façade of the old 'middle Co-op' near the top of Park Lane. This clock now adorns the entrance to the Anson Engine Museum.

He loved life in a coal mining village, especially observing all the workings and activities around the collieries. There was always plenty to keep him occupied - as a boy he was allowed inside the engine houses but only when they were winding coal not men. 'Big Ned', the huge Cornish pumping beam engine at Hockley, held a particular fascination. He and his friends knew it was pumping as they left the 'old school' (now the social centre) to go home, because the water in the brook behind the school would be discoloured and they would rush up to see it running.

The Old Co-op clock

He would listen intently at the miners 'stories', often told whilst waiting for a 'tuppenny haircut' at Billy Butterworth's stone cottage at Newtown. Billy was also the sawyer at Towers Yard, the administrative and workshop focus for all the collieries.

AN OLD PHOTOGRAPH OF LES TAKEN IN MARCH 1948

LES CAWLEYS WIFE ENA WITH WHOM HE SHARED
THE GREATER PART OF HIS LIFE AT THE ANSON.

The Cawley brothers with Reg Walters outside their home in Coppice Road, Poynton.

One of the many mature beech trees felled by Les in Poynton Park.

At the age of 13 he left school and found a job as a grocer's errand boy in Hazel Grove. He told a tale once about making a delivery when he was pedalling like mad up a steep hill and one of the bicycle pedals clipped the kerb - the groceries went flying - Les made a hasty delivery and even quicker getaway, but on return the shop keeper already knew that his customer had received several broken eggs!

When he was 17, Les was knocked off his bicycle and suffered a serious injury to his right arm, which had to be 'locked' permanently. Nevertheless he never allowed his handicap to interfere too much with the rest of his life, especially during his eventual career, which often involved much strenuous physical activity. (For example his keen interest in motor bikes which led him and his friends to acquire old bikes with which to 'ride around the fields'.) In addition, his skill with an axe was a 'work of art' to behold.

Around 1940 he got a job tree felling with Enouch Johnstone from Offerton. This set the pattern for his life. He bought an Ingeco engine and his boss commandeered it to drive a sawbench at Towers Park. When the 2nd World War finished he set up on his own, tree felling and supplying timber and logs, initially in the coppice close to Coppice Farm. He then bought from Lord Vernon, the former Anson pit site in 1947 and established the base for his business here. The Ingeco was set up with a sawbench and it is still at the Anson today.

Les married Ena Smith in 1960 and built his own house adjacent to the Anson. She was very much a character in her own right. She was a great support to him both in business and leisure; they attended countless shows together. She died in 2001 and her passing affected him deeply.

Having a wide range of equipment, including tractors and winches, Les was called upon many times to help others out who had got into trouble with sunken vehicles etc. He was always willing to help and he assisted at Poynton Show for many years, towing vehicles off the ground in wet years (and eating ice cream in hot years!) Les was a very good-natured and generous man. For a long time he used to supply needy folks around the village with free logs during the winter months. He was also unofficial, unpaid 'tree adviser' to Poynton Parish Council for well over 20 years.

He was largely a self-taught, self-sufficient individual. Having used and worked on many makes of tractors, cars, wagons, motorbikes and stationary engines he acquired a marvellous mechanical knowledge. His great interests were local history, mining and industrial archaeology, particularly in the fields of mining and engineering.

He had a wry sense of humour and a wonderfully 'infectious' chuckle. His memory was quite phenomenal, and he could remember the most incredible details of things past and present. Consequently he had a never-ending fund of true stories

1949 Fordson half track machine thought to have been owned and used by Les in connection with his business.

A Sanderson tractor with belt drive operating machinery in connection with Les's forestry work.

which he exchanged with his many friends and acquaintances.

He and Ena attended numerous steam rallies over the years, but when the engines got larger he decided it would be a good idea to let the public come to The Anson, and so a Trust was set up to enable a museum to be built. The first phase was built in 1986, and since then the museum has grown from strength to strength. It now houses the largest collection of stationary engines in the Country, and probably in Europe and receives visitors from all over the world. There is also a well-developed local history section.

The Anson Museum Trust consists of a small group of dedicated enthusiasts, ably led by Geoff Challinor, who now lives at The Anson. New members are always welcome. The museum is a registered charity (No 518587) and donations are likewise always welcome! It is the intention that the museum becomes an officially registered national museum within the near future. In 2003, Sir Nicholas Winterton MP agreed to become the Patron of the museum.

Les Cawley will be mourned for a long time - but this unique and friendly man has left a wonderful legacy to the village of Poynton - The Anson Engine Museum.

Born 6th December 1919 - died 5th July 2002.

Frame saw April 1953 used by Les to cut up the large trees he felled in connection with his business.

Construction work on the first museum building financed by Les on the site of the old Anson Pit.

VOLCANO

THE ARRIVAL IN MARCH 2003 OF A SIXTY TON RUSHTON VERTICAL ENGINE USED AS A GENERATOR DURING AND AFTER THE SECOND WORLD WAR BY ARP STUDIOS, PART OF EALING STUDIOS, DURING THE MAKING OF SUCH FILMS AS WHISKY GALORE, TRAIN OF EVENTS AND OTHER FAMOUS COMEDIES.   PICTURE BY JOHN SIMPSON.

MANCHESTER LINER.

THE ANSON ENGINE MUSEUM

Written by John Blowes for *The Power Engineer* Jan 2000 Vol. 4.

Just how advanced was the reciprocating engine 100 years ago?

Rather than carry out research at the library or on the web simply visit the Anson Engine Museum in Cheshire, where you can actually see a very impressive, operational, collection of engines and some driven machinery from this era.

Engineers will undoubtedly enjoy seeing the innovative ideas for fuelling, lubricating and governing these engines that can only really be appreciated by seeing the machines in operation.

Les Cawley, Geoff Challinor and several notable volunteers have renovated around 30 engine types built as early as 1886.

Typical makes:

Andrew	Hornsby-Ackroyd
Blackstone	National
Campbell	Robinson
Crossley	Ruston-Hornsby
Furnival	Tangyes
Gardner	Bates & Scholes
Mirrlees Bickerton & Day	

In fact over 20 engine makers were in existence within a 15 mile radius of the museum around this time.

Manchester was predominant in the development and manufacture, for at least seventy years after 1868, when Crossley Brothers first went into production. Crossley took up Otto and Langen patents to build atmospheric gas engines. Mirrlees Bickerton and Day, in Hazel Grove, concentrated on developing the light and heavy oil diesel engine and L. Gardner & Sons of Patricroft became known the world over for their role in bringing small, quality diesel engines to the industrial and marine markets.

By the turn of the last century oil and gas engines were in use - not only for electrical power generation, but with direct drives for all manner of applications - printing presses, lathes and even dentists drills!

Existing development of the electrical generator of course prompted diesel and gas engine popularity over the steam engine.

(Michael Faraday had produced one of the first simple, single pole generators in 1831 and by 1847, Charles Wheatstone had replaced permanent magnets with

Les supervises the construction of the first building stage of the Anson museum.

Partial structure of the first stage in progress.

The first prefab building on site, from a local school, in the first stage of the museum development.

An early picture of the old school prefab building showing the pit slag heap in the background.

Some technical terms we use- with a useful explanation of thier meaning

Phrase	literal meaning
☆!!?☆☆!	-- I SEEM TO HAVE CAUGHT MY HAND IN THESE GEARS
EEAAARRGG!	-- OH MY BUT THAT HURTS
STUPID MORONIC ·BRAINLESS CRETIN !!	- - - THAT PERSON HAS A LIMITED COMPREHENSION OF ENGINEERING TERMS
GET THE BLEEDIN' HAMMER TO IT!	Just ease it with a few gentle taps.
FWAUGHH!	- - - I find that female visitor to be quite attractive
YOU MUST BE !?T°☆ JOKING!	- - - I find what you are saying to be implausible
IT'S ABSOLUTELY KN••••••D	- - - This component appears to be mechanically defective
BZEZ MW ᙏ !	- - - I think Tony is having difficulty with electrical apparatus.
AARRGG!	It is adviseable to wear protectors.
CRUNCH EEEEEK!

TECHNICAL TERMS

electro magnets, which became self-exciting around 1857.)

The historian will be well aware however, of gaps in the collection.

* Otto-Crossley slide valve (1876-1888)
* Otto-Langden atmospheric (1867-1876)
* Lenoir (1860-1867)
* Bisschop Gas Engine
* Priestman Oil Engine

By 1913 these machines and developments of them became common place and a number of Chief Engineers formed the Diesel Engine Users Association - a respected body that presented papers covering shared problems and solutions. The Association evolved into the IDGTE that has continued to support development of the prime movers that we know today.

IDGTE wishes to support the museum in any way possible and should any of our readers have a lead on any of these missing engines, or indeed catalogues, tools or general information for any pre war engine, then we shall be pleased to hear from you.

Donations of engines and tools have been gratefully received from those engine makers still in business today, as well as from other companies and private collectors.

The museum is understood to have allocated far more floor area than any other UK museum to engines of this era and indeed it is the largest single collection in Britain and probably the largest in Europe that is open to the public.

The museum was granted Charity Trust status in 1987 and donations would be most welcome. Engines may be seen running most weekends between May and October 11.00 to 16.30 or by special arrangement. (Telephone to check) Or look on the Internet www.enginemuseum.org

OOPS!

THE ORIGIN OF THE NAME ANSON IN POYNTON

The name Anson refers to the pit, on the site of the museum, which was originally called Hig Meadow Pit. It was renamed after the marriage of the 6th Baron Augustus Henry Vernon to Lady Harriet Anson in 1851. The shaft of the pit collapsed in the 1950's and was backfilled with rubble as a safety measure and is currently fenced off.

The names of Warren, Bulkeley, Vernon and Anson appear today all around the Poynton area. These were the family names of the landed gentry who owned most of the land in Poynton and all of the coalmines. They lived a great life in some of the major halls and mansions, most of which have since been demolished, but their names live on in street names and public houses.

In order to see where the name Anson originated, that being the name of the pit, before the museum was built it might help to look at the descendants of Edward Warren who was buried in Stockport cemetery on the 10th September 1737.

Edward Warren's son George was created a Knight of the Bath on 26th May 1761. Sir George was the Member of Parliament for the district of Lancaster. He married his first wife Jane Revel in 1758 but she died three years later. He married his second wife Frances, the daughter of Sir Cecil Bisshopp on the 4th February 1764. Frances died 15th February 1804 following the death of her husband who died at the age of 67 on 31st August 1801.

On the 7th April 1759 his first wife Jane had given birth to a daughter Elizabeth Harriet who married the Seventh Viscount Bulkeley, Thomas James, on the 26th April 1777. They both took the name of Warren before that of Bulkeley. Thomas died on 3rd June 1822 whilst his wife Elizabeth died on the 23rd February 1826. They had not been blessed with any offspring.

Her estates were bequeathed to Frances Maria Warren, who was the daughter of Sir John Borlase Warren of Stapleford Nottinghamshire. Francis Maria was born 1784 and died 1837. She was married in 1802 to George Charles Vernon the 4th Baron from 1779 to 1835.

Their marriage produced a son George John Warren in 1803 who became the 5th Baron Vernon. He married his first wife Isabelle Caroline Ellison in 1824 and she produced a son Augustus Henry Vernon in 1829. He was to become the 6th Baron. On the death of Isabelle in 1853 George John remarried in 1859 to Frances Maria Emma Boothby who died 1907 having not had any children.

In 1851 Augustus Henry, the 6th Baron, married Lady Harriet Anson after whom he named the mine. Lady Harriet Anson lived from 1827 to 1898 and in 1854 she produced a son, the 7th Baron, whose name was George William Henry Vernon. In

National Gas and Oil Engine Co.

National Gas & Oil Engine Co. of Ashton-under-Lyne type NV S/No. 37934, built in 1929, 45 HP cold start four cycle crude oil engine. Used at the Walkerwood Reservoir.

National Gas and Oil Engine Co.

National Gas & Oil Engine Co. of Ashton-Under-Lyne S/No. 13639, built in 1905, Towns gas with tube ignition. Used in Margate.

1885 he married Frances Margaret Lawrance who was to produce two sons. The first was George Frances Augustus Vernon, the 8th Baron, born 1888. He sold off most of the western part of the estates in and around Poynton in 1911. He died 1915 and the second son, Francis Lawrance William Vernon, who was born 1889, became the 9th Baron. He sold off the rest of the Poynton properties in 1920. It would have been some years later that Les Cawley purchased the old Anson mine.

The 9th Baron was married in 1915 to Violet Miriam Nightingale Clay, and he died in 1963. He was succeeded by John Lawrence who became the 10th Lord Vernon, living in their home at Sudbury Hall. He married in 1955 to Sheila Marshal Clark and they had two daughters but their marriage was dissolved in 1982. He remarried in the same year to one Sally Stratford.

The hall at Sudbury passed to the National Trust in 1967 and the Vernon family moved to a smaller house on the Sudbury Estate.

On the death of the 10th Baron in 2003 the title passed to a distant cousin, Anthony Vernon-Harcourt a direct descendent of the 1st Lord Vernon.

Colliery winding engine at Park Pit in 1935
- similar to the one that was used in the Anson Pit.

The 11th Lord Vernon, Anthony Vernon-Harcourt, lives at Saffron Walden in Essex and has no connection with Poynton and the Warren Estate as he is not a descendant of Francis Maria Warren.

Care must be taken by visitors to our open days and appropriate clothing should be worn.

OPEN DAY

National Gas and Oil Engine Co.

National Gas & Oil Engine Co. of Ashton-Under-Lyne Type P S/No. 34313, built in 1924, 20 HP Towns gas with low tension magneto ignition. Supplied to and used in the University of Leeds, Mechanical Engineering Department for heat engine studies.

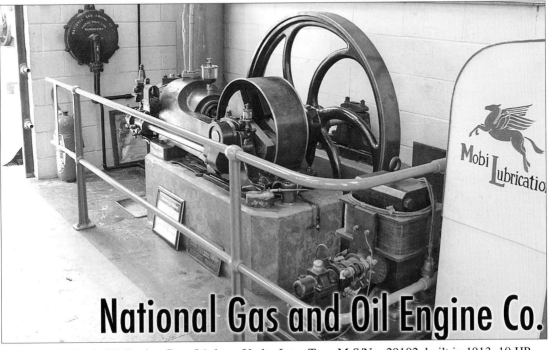

National Gas and Oil Engine Co.

National Gas & Oil Engine Co. of Ashton-Under-Lyne Type M S/No. 29102, built in 1913, 10 HP Towns gas with low tension ignition. Supplied to drive a generator at the Mechanics Institute, Crewe and then a teaching engine, at Crewe Technical College.

A ROYCE OF MANCHESTER CRANE INSTALLED IN MIRRLEES, HAZEL GROVE IN 1908.

HISTORY OF THE ANSON PIT
Taken from an article by D. A. Kitching in
Poynton a Coal Mining Village by W. H. Shercliff, 1990

The Anson Pit was originally known as Hig Meadow Pit and may have had a shaft situated just to the east of the Anson bungalow. In 1826 the winding engine was of the Newcomen atmospheric type having an 18-inch diameter cylinder, spur gears and flat rope drums fixed up in wood framing with a wrought iron boiler. There were 1088 yards of railroads underground and 22 coal tubs. It also had its own carpenters' shop.

Later that same year John Buddle, the well known colliery viewer from north-east England, reported on the condition of the collieries. His notes on the Hig Meadow Pit reveal it to have been 63 yards deep to the 5 feet mine (or seam) having been sunk beyond the crop of the 4 feet mine. Three levels were working on the north side - they were originally driven 360 yards to the Great Fault, but were now worked back again to within 100 yards of the shaft, with a breadth of working amounting to 75 yards. Only one level working back to the south - one hundred yards from the shaft. Eight coal getters were employed who worked about 7 quarters (just over 7 tons) per day. It was clear that there was only a small area left to work in the 5 feet mine and that the pit would require deepening to the Gees seam fairly soon.

By 1847 the pit was referred to as Anson or Lower Anson and employed 36 men and six boys underground working the Gees Seam at a depth of 132 yards. The winding engine was 16-horse power. In 1853 it was deepened to the Accommodation Seam at a depth of 191 yards whilst coal was also raised from the Reform level which entailed the cage being stopped at 147 yards. By 1856, 170 tons of coal per day were being raised.

Increased output was limited by the fact that the shaft was only 10 feet in diameter and could only take one cage, there being insufficient room for two to pass. The problem was neatly solved by Greenwell around 1866 when a bypass was constructed at the halfway point in the shaft. The bore was widened and fitted with iron conductors at this point and the two cages side-stepped each other in what must have been an odd experience for the miners riding to work. In conjunction with this work, a new winding engine was erected to replace the old machine which was reported to be in a dilapidated condition. This engine was set to work in May 1869 and performed very well until the colliery closed. It had two horizontal cylinders 25 inches by 60 inches with double beat valves. The drum was 14 feet in diameter for round ropes, raising two tubs per cage on one deck. An engine was later

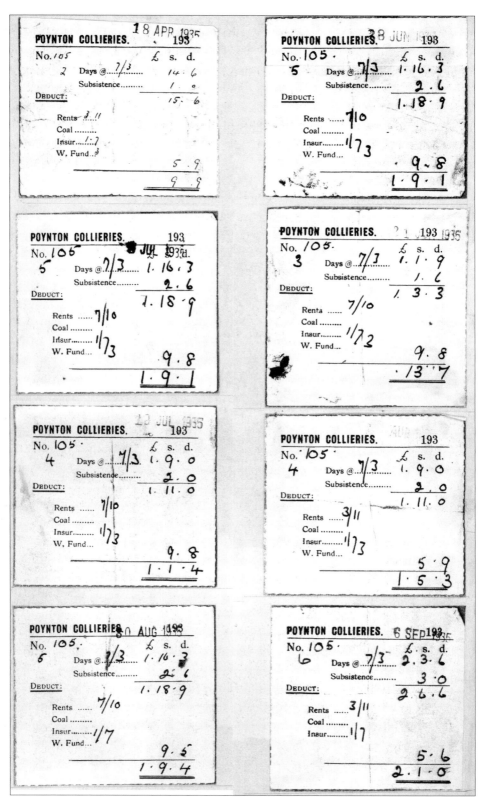

WAGES SLIPS SHOWING THAT THE MINERS EARNED
AS LITTLE AS £1.9S.1D FOR A FIVE DAY WEEK.

installed on the surface to haul sets of eighteen tubs for 900 yards up a 1 in 7 brow in the Accommodation Seam. It had two horizontal cylinders 15 inches by 30 inches geared 1 to 4 to a 5 feet diameter drum. Steam was supplied to both engines at 30 p.s.i. by three Lancashire boilers.

Compressed air coal cutters were introduced at the Anson Pit in 1922, to work the top block of the Accommodation Seam, but the pit was closed four years later and electricity was never used.

Ventilation for the Anson Pit was supplied by a furnace at Horsepasture Pit, SJ 941 841, and other ventilation furnaces were at Walker Pit SJ 937 836, Venture Pit SJ 947 831 and Higher Canal Pit SJ 949 839.

An interesting development at Anson Pit during the 1920s was the erection of a plant to extract oil from coal by a company unconnected with the collieries. This comprised a four storey building filled with retorts etc. and experiments were carried out with local and foreign coal as well as peat but it was closed by 1926 and operations transferred to Scotland. For several years this plant lay derelict with many barrels of oil lying around it.

Robey S/No. 33069 built pre-1913 Steam engine. Used for mine shaft ventilation at the Lady Pit, Poynton, bought by Lord Vernon.

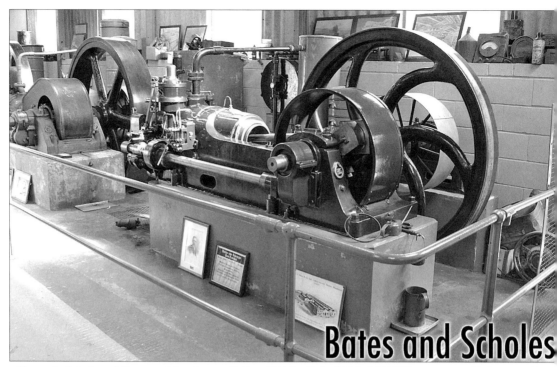

Bates and Scholes

Bates & Scholes of Denton, Manchester S/No. 5117 built in 1920, 34 HP Towns gas with low tension ignition. Used for wood turning machinery at Cornbrook Rd, Old Trafford, Manchester.

Tangye

Tangye of Birmingham S/No. 7684 built in 1906, 20 HP Towns gas with tube ignition. Clutha Paint & Oil Co., Paisley Rd, Glasgow, driving a paint mill.

Corngrinder

CORNGRINDER BUILT IN CONGLETON AND USED IN CREWE DRIVEN BY WATER WHEEL.

OPEN WEEKEND

THE LORD VERNONS

From *Poynton a Coal Mining Village* by W. H. Shercliff, 1990

In 1883 George William Henry Vernon became the 7th Lord Vernon after his father's death. In 1885 he married Frances Margaret Lawrance who came from New York, daughter of a rich banker. She tragically became mentally ill after the birth of her second son in 1889 (later the 9th Lord Vernon) and went to live in the South of France.

Not surprisingly, this much admired Lady's name, Lawrance, was used for the name of the new shaft at Park Pit which was completed in that year. It became the most productive of the shafts and greatly helped to raise the quantities of coal economically won. In 1890, 216,362 tons were raised (nearing the early peak of 1845) and profits averaged over £15,000 from 1886-97.

Poynton miners became much more heavily unionised from the 1890s when they formed their own Lodge within the Local District Association of the Miners Union and became involved in national strikes for the first time in 1893 and for four weeks in 1912.

In 1893 Lord Vernon joined the local Lancashire and Cheshire Coalowners' Defence Association which aimed to provide mutual support, combined action in disputes and strikes and regulated wages.

The Vernons continued to support the schools in Poynton with extensions in 1890 and 1899. The last Vernon and colliery promoted housing was erected from 1891-2 when 25 substantial cottages were built in Park Lane and London Road (recognisable from the terracotta date plaques). Some larger houses for office staff were included and a new post office for Poynton. The tradition of better than average housing for their workforce was maintained in the 1890s.

With the creation of more powerful local government bodies in the form of Parish and Rural District and County Councils at this time, it became beyond the powers of private individuals to maintain adequate standards of sanitation, sewerage, water supply (there were complaints of the pollution of Poynton Brook) and cheap housing for rent. The Liberal Lord Vernon welcomed the advent of these caring institutions and the more democratic control of local affairs. The Macclesfield Rural District Council provided a new outfall sewerage system for Poynton west of Chester Road where it crosses Norbury Brook.

The Vernons helped at times of the serious outbreaks of infectious diseases like scarlet fever by providing a cottage for an isolation hospital and gave lands for many of the sporting activities such as the Cricket Club, also acting as patrons.

In 1885 Lord Vernon, being concerned to promote opportunities for unmarried

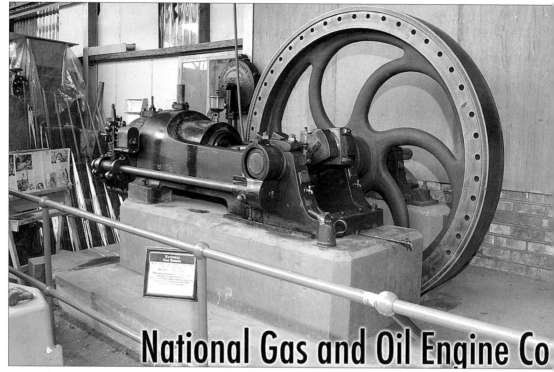

National Gas & Oil Engine Co. of Ashton-Under-Lyne Type SE S/No. 19867, built in 1909, 34 HP.
Found under railway arches when the Jubilee Underground line was being built.

National Gas & Oil Engine Co. of Ashton-Under-Lyne Type S S/No. 17659, built in 1908, 25 HP.
Sold to Liverpool University as a teaching engine.

girls and womenfolk in Poynton, arranged a lease with Edward Robinson Buck, already a shirt manufacturer in Manchester, to set up a factory in former stable buildings at Woodside, where the two inclines meet, to make sports shirts. This soon expanded using gas for energy from the colliery works nearby. It pioneered making guide and scout uniforms. Later Bukta became a household name for sportswear, tents and outdoor gear. The Vernons stayed at the Towers from time to time, but spent most time at their London residence, Sudbury Hall being let from the late 1890s until 1922.

In 1898 G.W.H. Vernon died prematurely at the age of 44 and was succeeded by his son George Francis Augustus, then only ten years old, who never married and was succeeded by his brother Francis Lawrance William in 1915.

This was a turning point in the Vernon connection with Poynton. At this time the economically winnable coal was running out and drainage problems were gradually becoming more acute. G.C. Greenwell Junior, who continued to manage the collieries and estate until 1920, was well liked by his workforce and with the support of his master moved with the spirit of the times, playing an important part in the Parish Council and many other societies and activities in Poynton.

Under the terms of his father's will the young heir became a ward of his aunt, the Honourable Adela Anson. He was educated at Eton and lived at the Towers with her and her husband, then Captain Anson. He astonished the village by leading a life of lavish entertainment and frequently being fined for speeding with his new motor car. Many stories are found in Poynton folklore of the older generation about his extravagances. However, he became for a time a member of the diplomatic corps.

In 1909 there was a coming of age celebration in Poynton with cannons roaring, the village decorated, a feast for 3000 on Poynton Green and a two-day party at which commemorative plates were again issued. There is one at Poynton Library with a handsome maroon edge, coat of arms and motto. This occasion was marred by too much drinking and bad behaviour. Many plates were skimmed over Poynton Pool and sank.

Captain Anson seems to have acted as adviser to the youthful Lord Vernon, acting as agent for the family until 1910. After this his health became poor and he died in 1913. The Stockport Advertiser noted he combined the finest qualities of an officer and gentleman and carried out many improvements in the village. He served on Macclesfield RDC, the Macclesfield Board of Guardians (for poor relief) and Cheshire County Council. He was a keen sportsman and started a rifle club.

At this time in carrying out the provisions of his father's will, the new 8th Lord Vernon had to take on the responsibility for the Vernon Estates. His father's will required that he purchase the contents of Sudbury Hall at valuation and also

Ruston Hornsby of Lincoln Type 6H S/No.146497, built 1927, 25 HP. University of Sheffield teaching engine

Ruston Hornsby to Hornsby Stockport design, S/No. 52263, built 1920, 140 HP
Producer gas low-tension. Sold to Thomas Niven, Carlisle to drive the saw mill.

purchase the colliery shares. The value of the agricultural part of the estates had deteriorated but the colliery share had risen sharply in value. This forced him to sell some part of his estate in order to buy other parts.

His first thought was to sell the Sudbury agricultural estate and live at Poynton but eventually in 1911 he decided to keep Sudbury and sell 863 acres of his Poynton Estate including the Towers, the park area and the western half of the estate which the catalogue describes as 'of more than ordinary importance being situate in a district of unusual charms yet within easy reach of the great industrial centres of Lancashire and Cheshire and thus presents unusual opportunities to Builders and Speculators in a district ripe for development and exceptional opportunities both to the agriculturalist and the investor'. The good shooting rights are also mentioned.

The sale realised £14,509. Lord Vernon enlisted very early in the First World War in the Derbyshire Yeomanry. He unfortunately caught dysentery in the Gallipolli campaign and died at the age of 27, being buried in Malta.

His brother Francis Lawrance William succeeded him as 9th Lord Vernon with his wife Violet Miriam Nightingale (Clay) whom he had married in 1915. He continued to manage the collieries and estate through G.C. Greenwell. Coal fetched a high price during the war and miners were well paid and kept fully at work after the government had taken ownership.

After the War pits returned to private ownership but owners faced great difficulties over low prices and at the same time great resistance to wage restrictions culminating in a long unsuccessful strike in 1921. The mining of coal at Poynton was becoming more and more uneconomic. In 1921 Lord Vernon relinquished complete control of the pits and Poynton Collieries was formed with George Harold Greenwell as agent to the Company, but their final decline led to closure in 1935.

In 1920 Lord Vernon decided to sell most of his remaining property in Poynton and in 1922 he and Lady Vernon took up residence at Sudbury Hall and began to restore it to its former elegance. The sale catalogue and accompanying map (copy in Poynton Library) give a great deal of information about the 1,573 acres and large numbers of properties sold, including four large private residences, Barlow Fold, The Paddock, Westfield and Oakfield, 11 farms in the eastern and southern parts of the original estate, with large numbers of cottages, smallholdings, the gas works, hat factory and shirt factory bringing in rents of £4,577 per annum.

Thus the long association of the Vernons with Poynton was ended and the way laid open for the estate to be broken up and developed a little before the Second World War and on a large scale in the 1950s to 1970s as a dormitory area for commuters and retired people. Fate had dictated that both the residences should be destroyed but fortunately the lake and park with its ancient trees were rented by the Parish Council and have remained an attractive park most valuable for leisure and community uses.

In 1963 the 9th Lord Vernon was succeeded by John Lawrance, who resided in a new house near to Sudbury Hall which with its beautiful grounds was given to the National Trust in 1971.

Footnote:

John Lawrance the 10th Lord died in 2003 and was succeeded by Anthony Vernon-Harcourt, the 11th Lord. He lives in Saffron Walden, Essex and has no connections with Poynton and the Warren Estate as he is not a descendant of Frances Maria Warren.

Scott of Haslington 2 cylinder cross compound Steam Engine, built 1906.
Sold to Horwich Railway Wagon Works. Came to Bartons Mill, Hazel Grove.
It was moved in the traditional method to the museum in 1984.

Ruston Hornsby

RUSTON HORNSBY OF LINCOLN TYPE 6XHRE S/NO. 168812 BUILT IN 1933, 36 HP DIESEL DRIVING A SAW MILL FOR WILLIAM SMITH BUILDERS AT NEWARK-ON-TRENT & REMOVED FOR PRESERVATION IN 1975.

FURNIVAL OF REDDISH. STOCKPORT S/NO.369 BUILT IN 1898, 2.5 HP TOWNS GAS WITH TUBE IGNITION CHAPEL-EN-LE-FRITH DRIVING A PLATEN PRINTING PRESS. A FURNIVAL PRINTING PRESS IS LOCATED BESIDE THE ENGINE AND THE FUTURE AIM IS TO HAVE THE ENGINE DRIVING THE PRESS.

A BRIEF HISTORY OF GARDNER

From *A Product History Over 125 Years*

James J. Francis 1995

The business was founded in 1868 by Lawrence Gardner in the cellars of four houses on Upper Drake Street in the Stretford area of Manchester. Initially the business was a 'Machinist' and 'General Engineer' but they soon developed their own products, such as Coffee Roasters and Dentists Chairs as well as Electric Motors and Dynamos.

Lawrence Gardner died in 1890, leaving his sons Thomas and Edward to run the business with their mother, later to be joined by brothers Lawrence, Ernest, Joseph and William. Although initially a Partnership, when a Company was formed, rather than Gardner Bros., they called it L. Gardner & Sons out of respect for their late father.

A move was made to larger premises in Lund Street and arrangements made to make A.E. & H. Robinsons' range of Hot Air Engines. This experience encouraged the design of internal combustion engines and the first of a range of horizontal 4-stroke Gas Engines was produced in 1894 with hot tube ignition. It is interesting to note that Hot Air Engines were made up to 1914.

The first I.C. engine was produced in May 1894, No. 81 (the previous 80 engines being Hot Air types), which was designated a No. 1 Gas Engine, developing 1 Horse Power at 350 R.P.M. and coupled to a generator. This was apparently used to light the 'small room' of the works.

The number of Hot Air and Gas Engines produced was low enough that both types could be numbered concurrently. Gardners' second Gas Engine, carrying the serial No. 82, had a bore of 3?" and was again used in the Works. A batch of six was produced in July 1894. In December 1894 the first No. 3 engine, Serial No. 101, was produced, having a bore of $5\frac{1}{2}$" and developing $3\frac{1}{2}$ B.H.P. at 250 R.P.M.

During 1894, L. Gardner & Sons were involved in a Court Case against William Butterworth, manufacturer of the 'Albert' Gas Engine, over patent rights. Gardners won the case, resulting in the William Butterworth concern going out of business. The surviving Albert Gas Engines bear a close resemblance to the early Gardner Gas Engines with eccentrically driven valve gear.

Development with use of paraffin oil started in 1896, resulting in the production of an Oil Engine with a small metering pump to supply the correct measure of oil to the vaporiser. By 1897 various sizes of Horizontal Engines were offered for sale with the oil pump and vaporiser.

The build up of engine sales for Gardners required a larger production capacity

SPRING CRUNCH

L. Gardner & Sons of Patricroft, Manchester Type 8HF S/No. 26965, built in 1926, 30 HP cold start heavy oil engine. Sold to G.Buxton & Son, 17 Steelhouse Lane, Birmingham. In 1968 it was dismantled and restored by Gardner & Sons and donated to the museum in the 1990's.

L. Gardner & Sons of Patricroft, Manchester S/No. 24759, built in 1921, 1.75 HP Petrol with high tension magneto. Drove a water pump supplying water to greenhouses at a nursery.

and land was bought in 1896 at Barton Old Hall on the outskirts of Eccles, Manchester. The move into the newly built workshops at Barton Hall Engine Works was completed in 1898.

The Gardner brothers were practical men who concentrated all their time on design or production and had no time or feel for selling. They relied heavily on their main selling agents, Norris & Henty - a partnership of Edward Hester Norris and Capt. Charles Gerald Henty.

Gardners' development continued on an evolutionary basis with ever improving modifications continually introduced.

As early as 1898 Gardners were experimenting with electric ignition by battery and coil and by 1902 Low-Tension ignition by magneto was available. The larger of the horizontal range were fitted for compressed air starting, the receivers being charged by the momentum of the flywheel after fuel was shut off.

The Gardner range of Suction Producers was offered for sale in seven sizes but few were sold.

The first vertical engine was made in 1898, developing 1.8 B.H.P. at 400 R.P.M. This was of open-crank form and the forerunner of the "V" range.

The thousandth engine was recorded in the Engine Book on the 2nd September 1899 as Engine No. 1432.

60% of all engines were exported, many going to France, Belgium, Germany, Spain and the Middle East.

The "M" series of four stroke vertical engines introduced in 1902 were primarily oil engines for marine use but were also made in spirit and gas versions for other uses such as stationary power use and rail and vehicle traction etc. Ignition was by low-tension magneto and igniters or hot tube. Many hundreds of these engines were built up to 1933. These were the early 'high speed' engines running up to 900 R.P.M. which set the pattern of Gardner reliability for marine use.

The 'V' type engines were introduced in 1903 specifically to satisfy domestic lighting and pumping requirements, as well as for general stationary power use, and could be built to use gas, petrol or paraffin.

These engines were produced until 1935 with the OVC, the OV with a compressor cylinder integral on the crankcase, until 1937.

An improved marine range designated the 'R' range was introduced in January 1906 with the IACR. The range was extended progressively until by early 1911 one, two, three and four cylinder versions of CR, ACR and BCR had been built.

By 1911, the continuing horizontal range was modified to the 'F' and 'H' form with petrol or spirit engines offered with H.T. magneto.

The rate of development in the first years of the century was dramatic and efforts were next made to develop the two stroke semi-diesel types.

L. Gardner and Sons

L. GARDNER & SONS OF PATRICROFT, MANCHESTER TYPE 4FHM S/NO.22702, BUILT 1918, 48 HP PARAFFIN ENGINE. USED AS A GENERATING SET AT HUNTINGDON HOSIERY MILLS, LEICESTER.

L. Gardner and Sons

L. GARDNER & SONS OF PATRICROFT, MANCHESTER TYPE 4T5, BUILT IN 1925, 75 HP GAS OIL ENGINE. ONE OF A PAIR FOR HUNTINGDON HOSIERY MILLS ADDING EXTRA GENERATING CAPACITY.

A.HARROP OF SHEFFIELD TOWNS GAS WITH HOT TUBE CONVERTED TO HIGH- TENSION IGNITION.
BUILT AS A GENERATING SET, BUT CURRENT GENERATOR ADDED BY THE MUSEUM. HISTORY UNKNOWN.

NATIONAL GAS AND OIL ENGINE CO.

National Gas and Oil Engine Co.

NATIONAL GAS & OIL ENGINE CO. OF ASHTON-UNDER-LYNE S/NO. 37708, BUILT 1920, 10 HP TOWNS GAS WITH HIGH-TENSION IGNITION. USED IN A TECHNICAL COLLEGE AS A TEACHING ENGINE.

These engines became very popular in the fishing fleets and could also be fitted with Gardner-made reverse gear and reduction gear boxes. For ease of starting Gardners were able to fit electric heaters in the domes. Water pumps and air compressors of Gardner design and manufacture were also available.

In 1912 the Norris & Henty sales agency had grown to such a size and importance to Gardners that it was decided to buy the partnership and form the new marketing subsidiary company of Norris Henty & Gardners Ltd. In the same year, recognising their dependence on suppliers, a new Iron Foundry was built on the Barton Hall site, capable of producing in the order of 250 tons of castings per month. It was at this period that the famous Gardner logo was introduced on all sales literature, documents, etc.

The Works were initially engaged in producing munitions for the 1914/18 War, when the labour force was supplemented by female labour. In 1917, of the 950 total work force 240 were women and girls.

By 1917, there came the need to produce the Ricardo designed Tank Engine. Gardners machined all the crankshafts on their own deigned C.P.M.s and a proportion of complete engines. Most of the existing engine builders produced these Tank Engines and Gardners' contribution was 375 complete engines. The engines were delivered over the period June 1917 to 1918 to the Director General of Mechanical Warfare Supply at Saltley, Oldbury, France, Leeds and Garforth.

The Gardner family had been responsible for a great amount of engine development since the early 1890s - changing the company from an average general engineering concern into an internationally respected Engine Manufacturer presenting a quality range of engines of all types and sizes for a steadily growing demand. In order to support these developments however a production capacity had to be built up to satisfy demand in quality and flexibility and of course cost effectiveness. Since the establishment of the Barton Hall Engine Works this aspect of the company had been the responsibility of Mr H E Hunter who led a highly effective team for over half a century.

From the start Barton Hall Engine Works was planned to be built of large shops with two or three fifty foot wide bays, most with overhead cranes. These bays were all numbered logically as 1 Bay 1, 1 Bay 2 -1 Bay 3 being the first shop on the site. This form was continued over the years with the last bay built used as the works canteen. This arrangement allowed for continuing expansion. The roadways between shops were named after the engine pioneers e.g. Akroyd Stuart Rd.

After the 1914/18 War, Gardners had a well-established range of engines for most applications and completed the range of 'VT' and 'T' types in the early 1920s.

This entry into the Compression Ignition Engines and experience in making their own Sprayers (injectors) used with Bosch injection pumps, undoubtedly

CAMPBELL OF HALIFAX S/NO. 5685 BUILT IN 1905. 10 HP TOWNS GAS CONVERTED TO HIGH TENSION MAGNETO IGNITION BERRY BROW PUMPING STATION, HUDDERSFIELD.

encouraged the extension of their smaller high speed ranges into the diesel type.

Development work under Joseph Gardner and his sons Hugh and John started in the mid 1920s. This was conceived as a Direct Injection Compression Ignition Engine with combustion chamber in the crown of the piston. The Gardner made multi-orifice sprayer was used in conjunction with the Bosch fuel pump.

First designed as a two-stroke cycle but finally a four stroke, the first engine of the 'L2' range was built in August 1929. It was exhibited at the Olympia Exhibition in London in September 1929 and later at the British Industries Fair at Birmingham in February 1930. Shown as a marine engine, the first 4 L2 engine, No. 28,203, had a bore of $4^{1/4}$" and a stroke of 6", developed 50 B.H.P. at 1300 R.P.M! The fuel economy was to set new standards for the engine builders over the next 40 years.

The cylinders were cast in blocks of two, with two blocks for the four-cylinder engine. The cylinder head was cast singly for each bore, each carrying the exhaust and inlet valves, motion levers and atomisers (later called sprayers). Each cylinder had a decompression lever. The crankshaft was fully machined from a solid forging, flanged at one end to carry the flywheel. Connecting rods were of steel forgings and drilled to carry lubrication oil from the big end to the small end. The crankcase was in two parts split across the centre line of the crankshaft. The lower crankcase carried the main bearings while the upper crankcase had large doors on each side allowing full access to the conrods etc. - particularly useful on marine applications. The lower crankcase could be of marine type with cast on mounting feet, while for motive use it carried machined faces for vehicle mounting. The flywheels were machined all over, balanced before assembly and machined to accept a shrunk-on starter motor ring.

Amongst visitors to the Olympia Exhibition was Trevor Barton of Barton Transport Ltd., a bus operator of Nottingham. He saw the potential for this engine in vehicular propulsion and immediately ordered a 4L2, No. 28,423, in February 1930, noted in the Engine No's book as - 'Marine footless type for vehicle, to be fitted into bus'.

The first 3L2, No. 28,433, was delivered to Wallis & Stevens as - 'Footless for Road Roller'.

Although orders steadily came through for marine use, the main interest was for vehicular use. F.H. Dutson of Leeds were the first to fit a 4L2, No 28,560, into a commercial vehicle - as a replacement for the petrol engine in an ex-RAF lorry in June 1930. Bartons ordered the first 5L2, No. 28,585, in June 1930.

Vehicular type L2 orders quickly followed from Thorneycroft of Basingstoke, Walsall Borough Tramway, Guy Motors of Wolverhampton, Peerless Lorries of Slough, Pickfords, T.S.M., Maidstone, Walker Bros. of Wigan, Crossley Motors of

Crossley Brothers

CROSSLEY BROTHERS OF OPENSHAW, MANCHESTER S/NO.145396. BUILT IN 1955, 16 HP TOWNS GAS WITH HIGH TENSION MAGNETO IGNITION. TEACHING ENGINE AT CHESTERFIELD COLLEGE OF TECHNOLOGY.

Crossley Brothers

CROSSLEY BROTHERS OF OPENSHAW, MANCHESTER TYPE GE112 S/NO.145173, BUILT IN 1955, 16 HP DIESEL. TEACHING ENGINE AT CHESTERFIELD COLLEGE OF TECHNOLOGY.

Crossley Brothers

CROSSLEY BROTHERS OF OPENSHAW, MANCHESTER S/NO. 39741, BUILT IN 1900, 9.25 HP TOWNS GAS CONVERTED TO LOW TENSION MAGNETO IGNITION TO DRIVE JOINERS & WHEELWRIGHTS SHOP AT HUDDERSFIELD.

Manchester, Karriers of Huddersfield, Marshall & Son of Grantham, Scammell, Watford, Leyland, and Fodens of Sandbach.

The full range of L2 engines was produced during 1930, being in 1, 2, 3, 4, 5 and 6-cylinder form. The range was completed in September 1930 with a 1L2 Stationary Engine.

Gardners' reaction to this high demand for a diesel engine to replace existing petrol engines in buses and lorries was immediate and continued development on a lightweight version of the L2. The famous 'LW' range was introduced with a 6LW built in July 1931, No. 29,150, which was booked to the London Office/Showroom for display.

The first 6LW to a customer was built in October 1931, No. 29,252, and delivered to Guy Motors of Wolverhampton. Sixteen more were built in 1931, and supplied to T.S. Motors Ltd, Peerless Lorries, Fodens, Walker Bros and others.

The power to weight ratio and fuel economy led the field for the next thirty years in the public transport and heavy goods areas. The 6LW gave 107 B.H.P. at 1700 R.P.M. and the 4LW delivered 71 B.H.P. at 1700 R.P.M.

Early experiments were made with diesel engined cars and a 4LW was fitted into the chassis of a 1925 Bentley - the first all British diesel engine car. This car was entered for the 1933 Monte Carlo Rally and, driven by Lord de-Clifford, achieved fifth place overall.

The LW Engine, although in the main made for automotive use in commercial and public transport vehicles was also supplied for marine use as well as for other special applications.

Modifications to improve the LW Engine were continually introduced without affecting interchangeability of parts and many vehicle performances were examined with the main chassis builders. One of the local test runs was up on Parbold Hill, between Southport and Wigan, having an average 1 in 12 gradient over a one-mile length.

To satisfy the increasing need for these more complicated aluminium castings a new Aluminium Foundry was built at Barton Hall Works in 1934. As well as sandcast crankcases, etc., die-casting was also set up to make, amongst other items, all the aluminium pistons required for the L2 and LW engines. The new foundry had a capacity of 100 tons a month.

For the light goods and passenger vehicles a smaller engine, designated the 'LK' was introduced in 1934, with a magnesium alloy crankcase and sump to further improve the power weight and power space ratios.

The marine and rail markets were not overlooked and a large 'L2' style engine was introduced with the 'L3' range to replace the older 'M' and 'CR' series which had become dated.

Gardner made 'UC' reverse gears and reduction boxes were available for marine use, as were the newly designed range of compressors and pumps.

The 1939/45 War broke out with the Gardner Works capable of a large contribution with its own products. The LW range went into general forces transport, particularly into Scammell Heavy Recovery and Tank Tractor vehicles, as well as into Power Generation units. The L3 was fitted into Air/Sea Rescue Craft and Motor Torpedo Boats. Marine and Transport engines continued to be made for the 'Home Front'. The most exciting contribution, however, must have been the fitting of the 4LK engines into the Midget Submarines.

Employment at the beginning of the War was 2,800, but the post-war demand for Gardner engines was such that a peak of 3,250 was reached in the late 1950s. These post-war years saw new machine tools, with the new 'Transfer' machines installed. New machine shop bays were built and the Aluminium Foundry extended. A new Iron Foundry 'Plate Shop' was opened in 1957.

Engine development continued, post-war, on the LW range and in the 1950s the 8LW was brought out to try and meet larger engine requirements and the horizontal versions of the LW were introduced to improve space use on buses, particularly the double deckers.

The markets, however, were changing beyond Gardners' abilities, with demands for motorway speeds and the new European weight standards and the UK truck, bus and engine manufacturers were steadily being out-played. This trend plus a disastrously long strike at Gardners over pay in 1973, lasting 13 weeks, eroded the long-standing goodwill with vehicle builders, who naturally sought alternative engine suppliers.

The downward trend in demand continued, and with the death of the two remaining grandsons, John and Hugh Gardner, the Board decided to seek a buyer for the Company. In 1977, agreement was reached with the Hawker Siddeley, Group, who sought to fit the Gardner range of engines into their existing Diesel Engine operations with Lister, Petter, etc.

From inception in 1930 to 1978, Gardners produced 184,914 High Speed Diesel Engines, including 90,475 LWs and 30,004 LXs.

Some re-tooling was done, particularly with automated crankcase and cylinder block machining, but unfortunately the design range was proving inadequate for the new demands. A late entry into Turbo applications of existing 'LX' engines helped, but completely new designs were really necessary.

The Hawker Siddeley Group, having difficulties of their own, sold the Gardner operation to Perkins Engines in 1986, who were looking to the bus range of engines and, of course, the quality name.

The reduction in demand continued and in 1993 Perkins Engines sold the

Robey

ROBEY TYPE 4P S/NO.14144. BUILT 1895. SENT TO BELFAST EXHIBITION TO GENERATE ELECTRICITY ON THE STAND OF COONEY & SWAN, 4 SKIPPER ST.

Hornsby Akroyd

HORNSBY AKROYD S/NO. 1383, BUILT 1896, 5HP. SOLD TO JOSEPH CLEAVE, MOULDSWORTH, CHESTER.

Company to the Texas Metal Group, who had previously purchased the foundries and the site.

Gardners, who recently completed their 125 years, continue to produce new and remanufactured engines for bus and marine application at Barton Hall Engine Works.

Postscript

During my time at Gardners machine Shops I worked on practically all types of their machine tools, centre lathes, boring mills, horizontal borers, crank pinning machines, planetary grinders etc. through to Automatics.

Being there for experience and not on 'Bonus Work' my skilled flat rate pay of £5.3s per 48-hour week enabled me to tackle the unpopular small batch work, which the piece workers tried to avoid. Most of this work was old type spares like CR type carburettor bodies, J type and HF type pistons up to $16\frac{1}{2}$" diameter, the hot bulb T type cylinder heads and the loose HF type breech with its spherical combustion chamber. Similarly in the Pattern Shop and Foundries, I worked on similar old style spares. My interest was awakened to the product history of the firm and I started collecting brochures & leaflets etc. on any of the old types going through.

In 1979, I became conscious of the Stationary Engine Rally interest and joined up, starting as everyone does with a Lister 'D'. In the following years I specifically followed up with Gardner Engines. When my old friend Jim Smith retired he had taken over an unwanted IBR and an IBM. His retirement interest was Longcase Clocks and having a few myself I did a swap. With Eric Broadstock I was able to renovate and get working these Gardner relics.

We soon learned that several old style engines previously collected by Dion Houghton for Gardners display became unwanted under the new Hawker Siddeley ownership and we were allowed to save them for rallying purposes. The 8HF Diesel was too big for us to handle so we arranged its transfer direct to the Anson Museum. The other engines were rebuilt and made to run by Eric and I and rallied for some years until finally they too were transferred to the Anson Museum for safe keeping and public viewing.

These and many other Gardner Engines are run for the enjoyment of the public at the Anson Museum and at Engine rallies all over Britain - and indeed the World. A continuing reminder of the wide range of engines produced over the last 125 years by L Gardner & Sons Ltd.

Left to right:

J.E.H. Andrew of Reddish, Stockport S/No. 7393, built in 1898, 21 HP towns gas with hot tube ignition. New to J.H.Pickup of Bury, then to J. Fields to drive a cornmill.

Blackstone of Stamford S/No. 159278, built in 1930, 32 HP spring injection diesel engine. Suffley clean water pumping station, near Sheffield.

Blackstone of Stamford S/No. 129455, built in 1914, 35 HP Lamp start paraffin engine. Drove a saw mill at Calver.

Campbell of Halifax S/No. 8961 built in 1912, 25 HP Lamp start crude oil engine. Used at Bollington water works.

LEAVING THE THREE TON FLYWHEEL SECURELY PROPPED UP—
WE WENT IN FOR LUNCH.

PROPPED UP FLYWHEEL

YOU CAN FEEL THE WEIGHT WE'VE
GOT ON NOW LES!

POLICE

SAND SCULPTURE